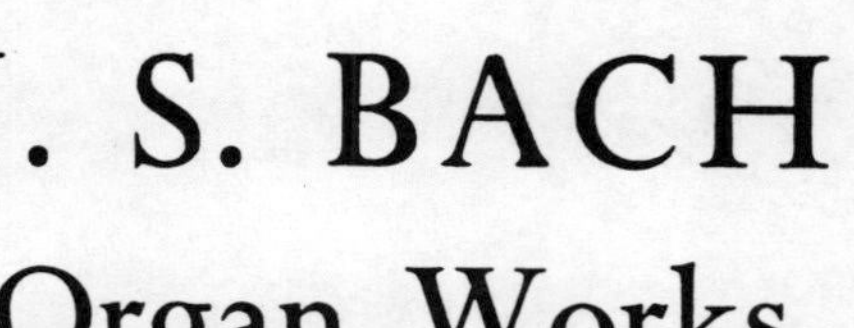
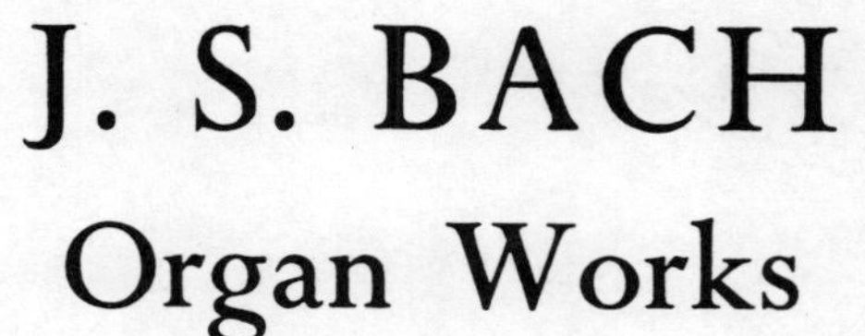

J. S. BACH

Organ Works

Book 2

PRELUDES, FUGUES & TRIO

Edited by Sir Frederick Bridge & James Higgs

NOVELLO PUBLISHING LIMITED
8/9 Frith Street, London W1V 5TZ

Order No: NOV 010001

PREFACE.

THIS Second Collection of Preludes, Fugues, and other Pieces, is designed to follow in progressive difficulty the Eight Short Preludes and Fugues already issued.

The ALLABREVE IN D MAJOR is marked, as in the original, "*Organo Pleno,*" and the present may be a convenient opportunity for offering a few remarks on this and the kindred term "*Organo Pieno.*"

The natural equivalent of the expression is "Full Organ," and in some cases, no doubt, Bach's intention will be best fulfilled by playing the composition so marked on the full power of the organ. The character of the Allabreve justifies such treatment, but inasmuch as the expression is employed by Bach in connection with pieces of exceedingly diversified character—as the Prelude in E♭ commonly prefixed to the St. Ann's Fugue, the Grand Prelude in B minor, and the Toccata in D minor (Dorico)—it is evident the expression must have some further signification, and it is suggested that the true meaning is rather "*Complete Organ,*"—in fact, that the use of this expression indicates that the composition demands an instrument of *full* resource.

CANZONA IN D MINOR.—The description generally given of a Canzona is that it is a species of Madrigal. The term, applied to instrumental music, originally seems to have indicated a composition wherein the imitation was more fragmentary than is the case in a genuine Fugue. In examples from Frescobaldi the theme is frequently varied at each fresh series of entries, and this feature, rather than fragmentary treatment, would seem the justification for the name assigned to this beautiful but too little-known organ piece. The student cannot fail to be interested in noticing the variation both subject and countersubject undergo, at the point where the movement changes from common to triple time.

FUGUE IN D MINOR.—This Composition is included in the present series as being of a convenient grade of difficulty, although it more properly belongs by classification to the Choral Preludes. It is founded on the Chorale "*Wir glauben all' au einen Gott.*" The composition is almost unique as regards form, being fugually constructed as regards the three upper parts while the pedal sustains an independent figure, the movement of which has doubtless procured for this work the popular title of the "Giant." This, like the Allabreve, is marked "*Organo Pleno,*" and may be effectively played on a loud organ.

FUGUE IN E MINOR.—The general plan of this edition of Bach's Organ Music is, as has been already explained,* to place all that is to be played by the right hand on the upper of the two mànual staves, and all that is to be played by the left hand on the lower of the two manual staves; yet in this Fugue, and in one or two other indicated, or self-evident cases, the too stringent application of the rule is relaxed to save needless changes of clef.

Many editions of this Fugue wholly omit the Mordent that Bach wrote. It seems to us so characteristic of, and essential to, the subject that we have retained it, and we avail ourselves of the present occasion to remark that whenever a shake or other grace is introduced as a part of the initial theme it should also appear at each subsequent entry.

It may not be out of place to caution the student carefully to distinguish between the signs 𝆖 and 𝆗.

𝆖, the mordent, in all but purely exceptional cases, is made with the lower auxiliary one semitone below the principal note. †

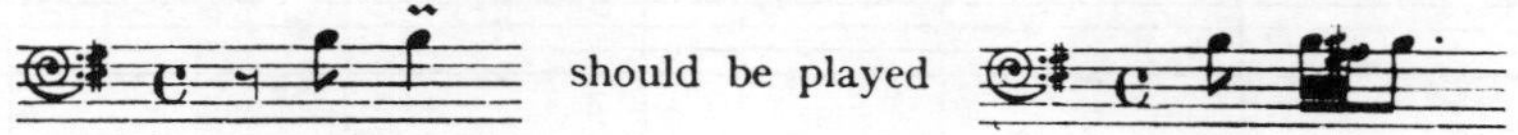

𝆗, the beat or inverted mordent, is made with the upper auxiliary—

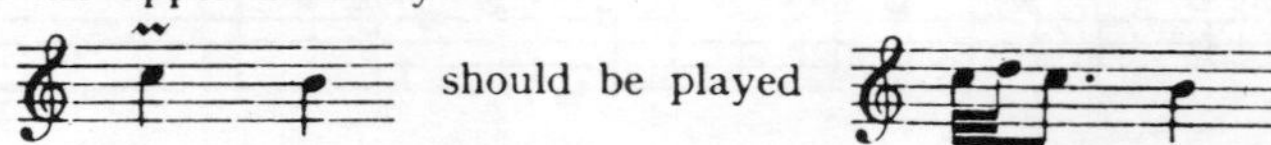

THE TRIO IN D MINOR has been included in this book because the student will find the practice of trio-playing on the organ of the highest importance, and we have thought it desirable an early opportunity should be afforded for the practice of the incidental difficulties. This Trio had, in the original, many graces and embellishments quite alien to the present habits of organ-playing: some of these we have ventured to omit. It may be effectively performed on any soft stops, if care be taken to contrast the *quality* while maintaining the just *balance* of the two manuals employed.

J. F. B.
J. H.

SUGGESTED METRONOMIC RATE.

Allabreve, D Major	page 26 ...	𝅗𝅥 = 80.
Prelude, G Major	,, 30 ...	𝅘𝅥 = 80.
Canzona, D Minor	,, 34 ...	C 𝅘𝅥 = 84.
,, ,, ...	,, 35 ...	3/2 𝅗𝅥 = 72.
Fugue, D Minor	page 38 ...	𝅘𝅥 = 69.
Fugue, G Minor	,, 41 ...	𝅘𝅥 = 60.
Prelude, E Minor	,, 44 ...	𝅘𝅥 = 60.
Fugue, ,, ...	,, 46 ...	𝅘𝅥 = 66.
Prelude, C Minor	page 48 ...	𝅘𝅥 = 60.
Fugue, ,, ...	,, 50 ...	𝅘𝅥 = 63.
Trio, D Minor	,, 54 ...	𝅘𝅥𝅮 = 96.

* *See* Preface to Book I.

† The student may with advantage consult Mr. Dannreuther's exhaustive work on Musical Ornamentation. It is right to add that Mr. Dannreuther favours the diatonic treatment in this case.

*

ALLABREVE.

BWV 589

✝) See Preface.

PRELUDE G MAJOR.

BWV 568

dim.
Reduce to
Diap?

cresc.

ff
Full.

CANZONA D MINOR.

BWV 588

cresc.
add 4 ft.

tr
(Adagio.)

FUGUE D MINOR.

(THE GIANT.)

BWV 680

Organo Pleno (Full Organ.) ✣)

✣) See Preface.

8 2
1 4

FUGUE G MINOR.

BWV 131ᵃ

5
3

Pt F 4'05"

PRELUDE and FUGUE E MINOR.

BWV 533

cresc.
ff
Full.

FUGUE.
8 & 4 ft.
with Sw.
R. H.
cresc.

dim.
ff
Full
ff

PRELUDE and FUGUE C MINOR.

BWV 549

FUGUE.
Diaps 8 ft
R.H.
tr
L.H.

tr
tr
tr
add 4 ft

ff
ff

tr
dim
Diap^s

TRIO.

BWV 583

+) See Preface

J S BACH ORGAN WORKS

BOOKS 1, 4 & 5 - *EDITED BY JOHN DYKES BOWER AND WALTER EMERY*
BOOKS 2, 3, 6 TO 12 - *EDITED BY SIR FREDERICK BRIDGE AND JAMES HIGGS*
BOOKS 15 TO 20 - *EDITED BY SIR IVOR ATKINS AND OTHERS*

(The BWV numbers are given in brackets)

BOOK 1: EIGHT SHORT PRELUDES AND FUGUES (553-560)

BOOK 2: MISCELLANEOUS
Allabreve in D major (589)
Prelude in G major (568)
Canzona in D minor (588)
'Giant' Fugue in D minor (680)
Fugue in G minor (131a)
'Little' Prelude and Fugue in E minor (533)
Prelude and Fugue in C minor (549)
Trio in D minor (583)

BOOK 3: MISCELLANEOUS
Five-part Fantasia in C minor (562)
Fugue in B Minor on a subject by Corelli (579)
Prelude and Fugue in A major (536)
'Short' Prelude and Fugue in C major (545)
Fantasia and Fugue in C minor (537)
'Little' Fugue in G minor (578)

BOOK 4: SONATAS FOR TWO MANUALS AND PEDALS
Nos I-III (525-527)

BOOK 5: SONATAS FOR TWO MANUALS AND PEDALS
Nos IV-VI (528-530)

BOOK 6: MISCELLANEOUS
Toccata and Fugue in D minor (565)
Prelude and Fugue in D major (532)
Prelude and Fugue in F minor (534)
Prelude and 'St Anne' Fugue in E flat (552)

BOOK 7: MISCELLANEOUS
'Great' Prelude and Fugue in A minor (543)
'Great' Prelude and Fugue in B minor (544)
'Great' Prelude and Fugue in C minor (546)
Prelude and Fugue in C major (531)
Prelude and Fugue in G major (550)

BOOK 8: MISCELLANEOUS
Toccata in C (or E) (566)
Prelude and 'Wedge' Fugue in E minor (548)
'Great' Prelude and Fugue in G major (541)
Prelude and Fugue in G minor (535)
Fantasia and Fugue in G minor (the 'Great' G minor) (542)

BOOK 9: MISCELLANEOUS
Toccata in C major (564)
Prelude and 'Fiddle' Fugue in D minor (539)
'Great' Prelude and Fugue in C major (547)
Fantasia in G major (572)
Toccata and Fugue in F major (540)

BOOK 10: MISCELLANEOUS
'Dorian' Toccata and Fugue in D minor (538)
Prelude and Fugue in A minor (551)
Passacaglia and Fugue in C minor (582)
Fugue in C minor on a subject by Legrenzi (574)
Prelude in A minor (569)

BOOK 11: FOUR CONCERTOS
(Arrangements of Violin Concertos by Antonio Vivaldi)
Concerto No 1 in G major (592)
Concerto No 2 in A minor (593)
Concerto No 3 in C major (594)
Concerto No 4 (in C major (595)

BOOK 12: MISCELLANEOUS
'Jig' Fugue in G major (577)
Fantasia and Fugue in A minor (561)
Fantasia, with imitation, in B minor (563)
Fantasia in G major (571)
Fugue in D major (580)
Fugue in G major (576)
Prelude in C major (567)
Fantasia in C major (570)
Prelude in C major (943)
Fugue in C minor (575)
Fugue in C major (946)
Pastorale (590)
Trio in C minor (585)
Aria in F (587)

BOOKS 13 & 14:
Now discontinued, these books contained selected Chorale Preludes which are in Books XV to XIX.

BOOK 15: ORGELBÜCHLEIN (The Little Organ Book)

BOOK 16: THE SIX 'SCHÜBLER' CHORALE PRELUDES AND PART III OF THE CLAVIERÜBUNG

BOOK 17: THE 'EIGHTEEN' CHORALE PRELUDES

BOOK 18: MISCELLANEOUS CHORALE PRELUDES (PART I)

BOOK 19: MISCELLANEOUS CHORALE PRELUDES (PART II) AND VARIATIONS

BOOK 20: FOUR-PART HARMONIZATIONS OF THE CHORALES USED IN THE ORGAN WORKS